This book belongs to

Suggestion on how to use this book
Unlocking the Magic of Rumi's Poetry with a Child

This book invites you and the young ones in your life on a captivating journey through the world of Rumi's poetry.. Infused with metaphor and layered with meaning, Rumi's poems offer unique experiences to each reader. Just like snowflakes, no two interpretations are ever exactly alike. This is part of the magic!

At the back of the book, you'll find a helpful guide to assist you in unpacking the wisdom and wonder within each poem. This guide includes "possibilities," offering one interpretation as a potential starting point for discussion. Additionally, three thought-provoking questions accompany each poem, encouraging curiosity and exploration.

As you share these poems with a child, focus on their unique experience. What do they hear, see, and feel through the words and images? The book isn't just about teaching children to understand metaphors, it's about empowering them to experience the magic of language, where words can touch our hearts in unexpected ways.

Remember, this journey isn't limited to children. The young at heart are welcome too! So embark on this adventure together, embracing the joy of shared discovery and the endless possibilities within Rumi's words.

Project Shift, LLC.
Copyright © 2024 DJ Kadagian.
Rumi for Kids- and the Young at Heart / DJ Kadagian
ISBN: 979-8-985484-21-9 (Paperback) - ISBN: 979-8-985484-9-24 (Hardcover)
Book design by Project Shift - Printed in the United States of America.

www.Project-Shift.com

RUMI for Kids

and the young at heart

Over eight hundred years ago, in a land far away called Persia, lived a very special boy named Jalaluddin Rumi. His father was a famous leader and teacher in the community, and Rumi was expected to follow in his footsteps. As he grew older, he too, became a wise and deeply loved teacher and mystic.

But then, one day, something magical and unexpected happened! Like a shooting star across the night sky, a strange and enchanting mystic called Shams-i-Tabrizi arrived. A whirlwind of wisdom and laughter, Shams challenged Rumi to see the world not with his eyes but with his heart. He spoke of love like a hidden language, a secret music waiting to be played. Though many in his community disapproved, Rumi, drawn by an invisible thread, dropped everything to follow Shams, leaving comfort for the unknown.

Shams was like a patient gardener, nurturing the seeds of wisdom in Rumi's soul. For three years, they were two branches on the same vine, inseparable and swaying in the wind of shared laughter and secrets.

Then, on a chilly December night, while they were deep in conversation, a mysterious call came for Shams at the back door. Like a character in a fairy tale vanishing into the night, Shams stepped out into the darkness and was never seen again, leaving behind a story wrapped in mystery.

Heartbroken, Rumi would search for Shams for years but would never find him. Over the course of twelve years, he poured his love and loss into words like liquid gold. He began writing poems so beautiful, so filled with longing and joy, that they seemed to dance and sing. Though Shams was gone, his spirit echoed in every verse. Even though he lived a very long time ago, Rumi's words are as moving and powerful as when he wrote them and make many people feel happy and understood even to this day.

Do not be satisfied with stories, how things have gone for others.

Unfold your own myth

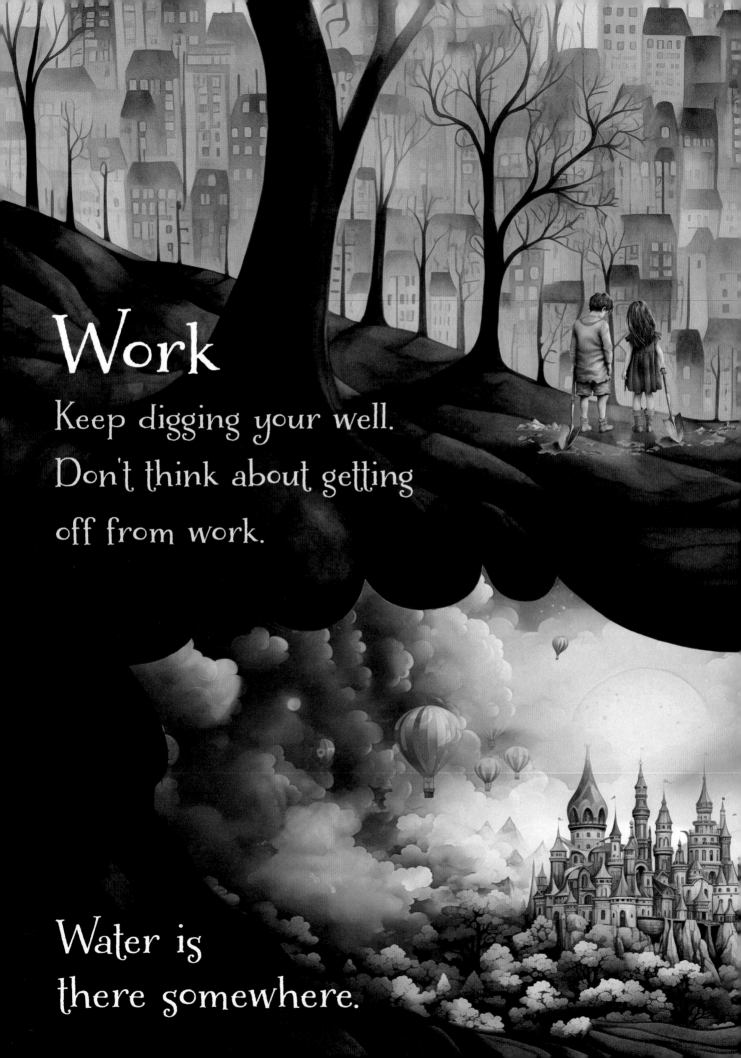

Work

Keep digging your well.
Don't think about getting
off from work.

Water is
there somewhere.

Keep knocking,
and the joy inside will
eventually open a window
and look out to see
who's there.

The morning wind spreads
its fresh smell.

We must get up and take that in,
that wind that lets us live.

Breathe before it's gone.

When someone
is counting out
gold for you,

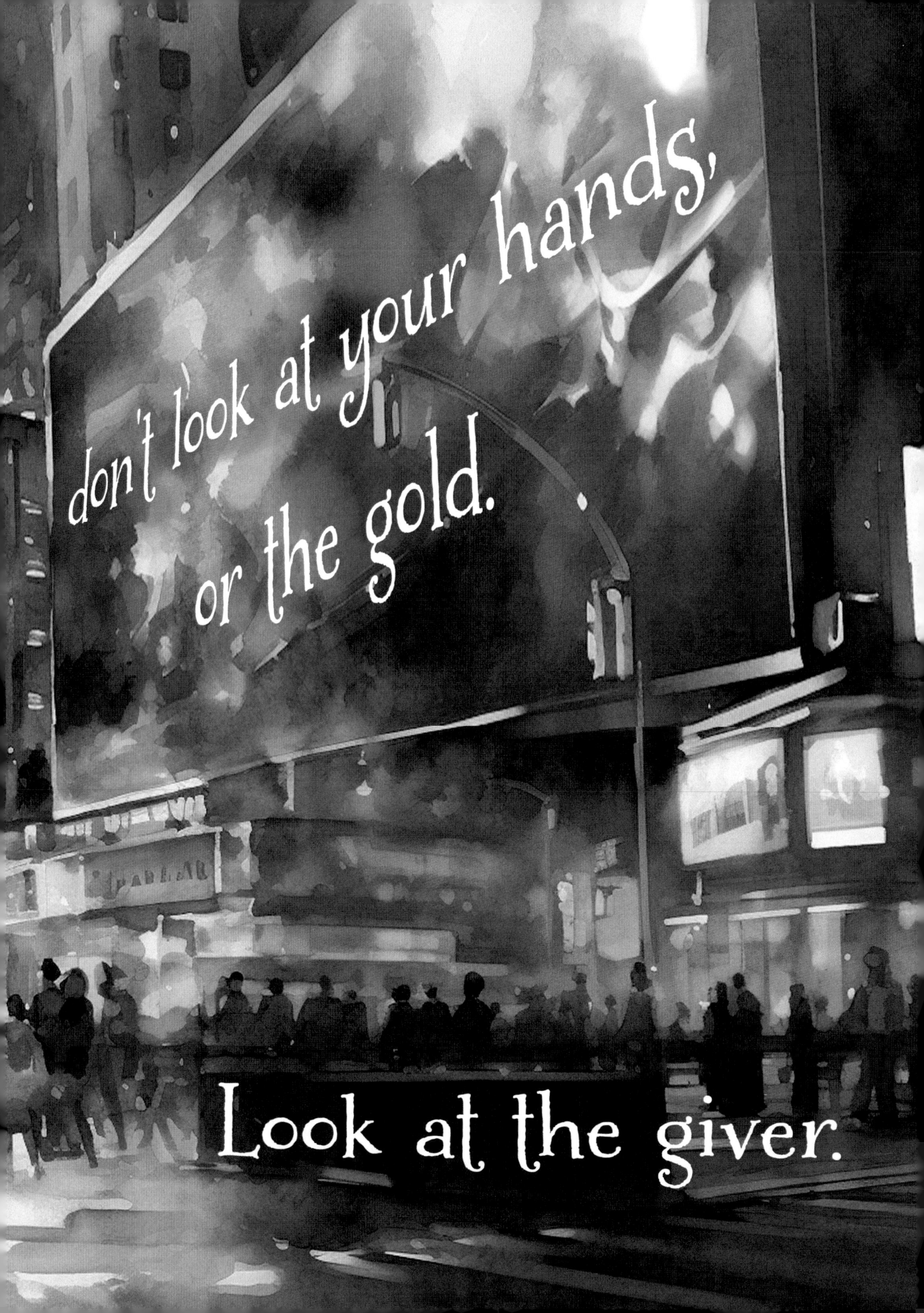

don't look at your hands,
or the gold.

Look at the giver.

Be empty of worrying.

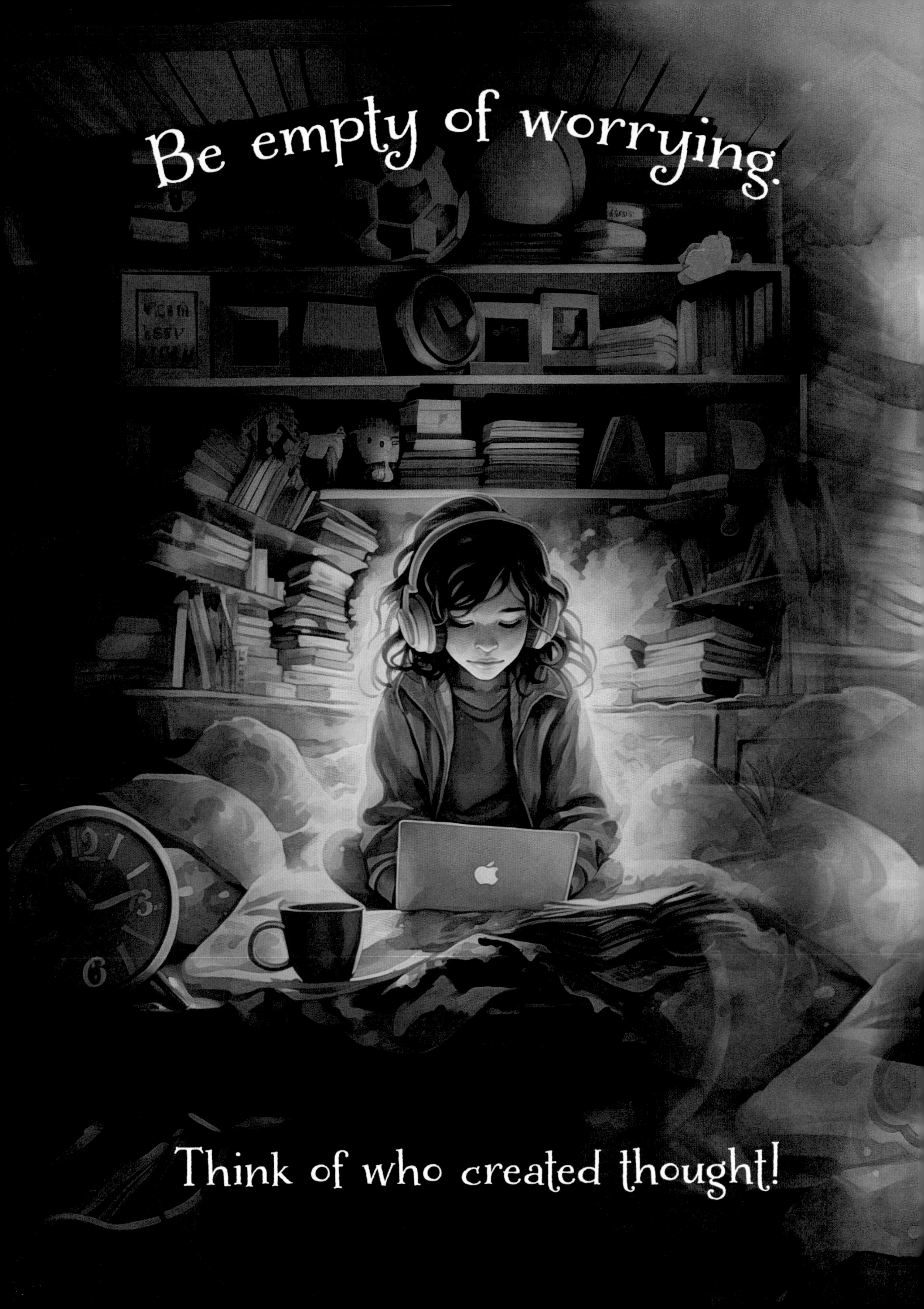

Think of who created thought!

This being human
is a guest house.

Every morning
a new arrival.

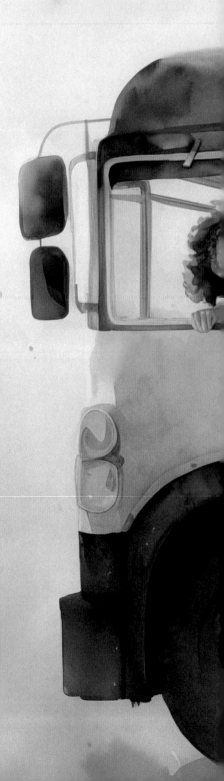

Be grateful for whoever comes,
because each has been sent
as a guide from beyond.

In your light I learn how to love.

In your beauty, how to make poems.

You dance inside my chest,

where no one sees you,

but sometimes I do,

and that sight becomes this art,

The ocean
takes care of
each wave

till it gets to shore

I am so small I can barely be seen.

Look at your eyes. They are small,

But they see
enormous things.

How can this great
love be inside me?

The breeze at dawn
has secrets to tell you.
Don't go back to sleep.

You must ask for what
you really want.
Don't go back to sleep.

People are going back and forth across the doorsill where the two worlds touch.

The door is round and open.
Don't go back to sleep.

When you do things
from your soul,
the river itself
moves through you.

Freshness
and a deep joy
are signs of the current.

Out beyond ideas
of wrongdoing and rightdoing
there is a field.

I WILL MEET YOU THERE.

When the soul lies down in that grass
the world is too full to talk about.

What was said
to the rose that
made it open,

was said to me
here in my chest.

Doves when they call coo,
are looking for us.

Nightingales and parrots
change their perches hoping to
be nearer to us.

Word of us reached the fish.
They swerved and leapt.
Waves from that stirring
keep coming in.

The soul has been given
its own ears to hear things
that the mind does not understand.

A mountain keeps an echo deep inside itself.

That's how I hold your voice.

Let the beauty we love
be what we do.

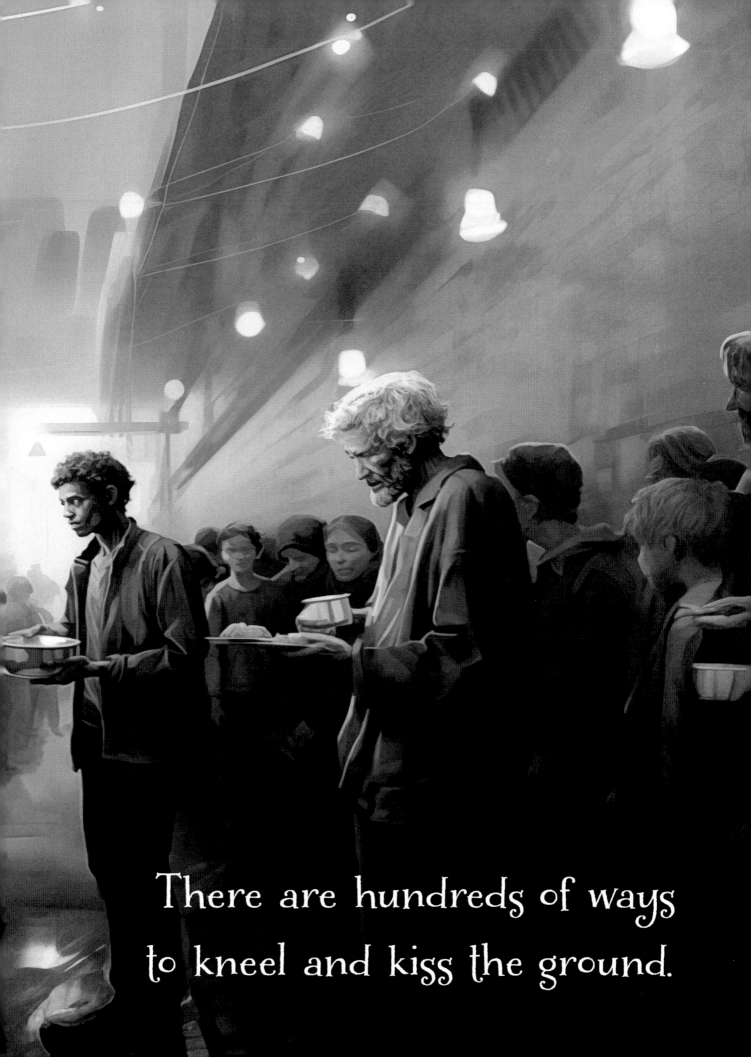

There are hundreds of ways
to kneel and kiss the ground.

Maybe in your loud confusion
the world will disappear
and the curtain will lift.

I tell everything,
but I do not say it,

because, my friend,

it is better that your secret
be spoken by you.

The sun's
light looks a little
different on this
wall than it does
on that wall.

And a lot different
on this
other one,

but it's still
ONE LIGHT.

The moon has opened its face
and its wings made of light.

Borrow eyes to see this, if yours cannot.

Listen to presences
inside poems.

Let them take you
where they will.

Follow those private hints.

Unlocking the Magic of Rumi's Poetry

On the following pages you will find a helpful guide to assist you in unpacking the wisdom and wonder within each poem. We have included a thumbnail of each illustration with its corresping poem next to it. Below that you will find a "possibility," offering one interpretation of the poem as a potential starting point for discussion. And in the blue box, we have included three thought-provoking questions encouraging curiosity and exploration.

As you share these poems with a child, focus on their unique experience. What do they hear, see, and feel through the words and images? This book isn't just about teaching children to understand metaphors, it's about empowering them to experience the magic of language, where words can touch our hearts in unexpected ways.

Remember, this journey isn't limited to children. The young at heart are welcome too! So embark on this adventure together, embracing the joy of shared discovery and the endless possibilities within Rumi's words.

Do not be satisfied
with the stories that come before you.
Unfold your
own myth.

This poem is like a gentle nudge saying, "Don't just listen to all the stories about what other people have done and who they are. Imagine you're the hero in your own storybook. The poem encourages you to be yourself and make up your own exciting tales, using your imagination to go on adventures that no one else has thought of before.

❀ Why do you think the poem tells us not to just listen to other people's stories? Have you ever wanted to do something different from everyone else?
❀ The poem says not to be "satisfied" with stories that come before you. Do you think that means you shouldn't listen to any stories at all? Or maybe it means you can use those stories as inspiration, but then add your own twists and turns to make them even more awesome?
❀ What if you could make up your own superhero or princess story, completely different from any you've heard before? What special powers would your hero have? Where would their adventure take them?

Work. Keep digging your well.
Don't think about getting off from work.
Water is there somewhere.
Keep knocking, and the joy inside
will eventualy open a window and look out to see who's there.

This poem is kind of like cheering you on when you're trying something hard. Imagine you're digging a hole in the backyard, looking for buried treasure or a magical lost city. The poem says to keep digging, even if you get tired or think you won't find anything. Remember, the good stuff (like the treasure or cool water) might be hidden deep down, so don't give up easily! It's also like saying that doing something you care about, even if it's tough, can lead to happiness in the end. It's like knocking on a door to a fun surprise party – you might have to wait a bit, but eventually, something amazing will appear!

❀ The poem says you shouldn't think about getting off from "work." Do you think this means never having fun or taking breaks? Or maybe it means focusing on something you really care about, even if it's not always easy? What are some things you enjoy doing, even if they take effort?
❀ The poem says "Keep knocking, and the joy inside will eventually open a window." Did you ever make a new friend by being friendly and saying hi even when they seemed shy? This poem is like that! It says doing good things and putting in effort can lead to happiness and new connections, even if it takes time. What are some ways you can "knock" on joy's door today?
❀ Why do you think "joy" would look out a window to see who's there? How do you feel when you finally finish something you've been working hard on?

The morning wind spreads its fresh smell.
We must get up and take that in,
that wind that lets us live.
Breathe before it's gone.

This poem is like a wake-up call for your senses! It's saying that the very first breath of fresh morning air is like a special gift, full of energy and life. It's encouraging you to jump out of bed and really pay attention to that feeling. The poem also wants to remind us to appreciate the simple things that make life beautiful and that every day is a new chance to experience amazing things, so don't waste it sleeping in - go out and explore before the day disappears!

❀ Imagine the morning wind isn't just air, but a whisper from something much bigger, like a giant friend you can't see. What kind of things would that friend whisper to you in the morning? Would they tell you to be kind, be brave, or chase your dreams?

❀ How does fresh air in the morning make you feel? Why do you think it's important to notice things like the morning air, instead of rushing through your day?

❀ The poem talks about breathing in the wind before it's gone. Why is it important to enjoy things while they are here? Are there other things in your life you try to appreciate while you have them?

When someone is counting out gold for you,
don't look at your hands,
or the gold.
Look at the giver.

This poem is like a special reminder that when someone is giving you something precious, like gold, it's not just about the shiny, valuable thing you're getting. It's really important to pay attention to the person who is giving it to you. This is because being thankful for the kindness of the person who is sharing with you is even more valuable than the gift itself. It's like when someone gives you a present, the best part isn't always what's inside the box, but the love and thoughtfulness from the person who gave it to you. So, the poem tells us to appreciate and be grateful for the people in our lives, not just the things we receive.

❀ Imagine you're at your friend's house and they come out of the kitchen with a big pile of warm, delicious cookies. The poem says not to look at the cookies right away. Instead, you should look at your friend. Why do you think that is?

❀ Can you think of a time when someone's kindness made you feel really special, even more than a present they gave you?

❀ What do you think this poem is trying to teach us about being thankful?

Be empty of worrying.
Think of who created thought!
Why do you stay in prison
When the door is so wide open?

This poem is like friendly advice telling us not to spend too much time being worried or scared about things. Imagine your mind is a room, and worrying is like a chain that keeps you locked up inside. But the poem asks us to remember something amazing: we have the power to think and imagine, which is like having a key to that room. It's wondering why we choose to stay locked up when we could just open the door and walk out into a big, exciting world.

✽ Why do you think the poem suggests that worrying too much is like locking ourselves in a prison, and how can we use its advice to feel happier?
✽ In the poem, there's a part that talks about thinking of who created thought. Why might remembering who created our ability to think help us to let go of our worries and fears?
✽ When the poem mentions that the door is so wide open, what are some ways you think we can 'open the door' and escape from feeling trapped by our worries?

This being human is a guest house.
Every morning a new arrival.
Be grateful for whoever comes,
because each has been sent
as a guide from beyond.

Imagine your mind is a place where people gather, like a home or your school where big yellow buses come to drop kids off every morning. Every day, new thoughts and feelings arrive, like travelers from faraway lands you've never seen before. Some wear brightly colored clothes and speak unfamiliar languages, full of energy and excitement. Others might be quieter, shrouded in cloaks of mystery, carrying wisdom gathered on long journeys. This poem whispers, "Welcome them all!" Even the passengers who seem strange at first are there for a reason. Each one, no matter how unexpected, holds a piece of knowledge or a new way of seeing things.

✽ The poem makes us think of our mind as a place where people, like thoughts and feelings, come and go. Why do you think imagining our mind like this is helpful? How does it change the way we look at our thoughts?
✽ Thoughts and feelings are described as different kinds of travelers in the poem. How would you welcome both the exciting and the quiet ones into your mind? What can we learn from even the ones that seem strange at first?
✽ Every thought and feeling is said to bring us something valuable, like a new idea or perspective. Why do you think every visitor to our mind is important, even if they're unexpected? Can you think of a time when a surprising thought or feeling helped you understand something new?

In your light I learn how to love.
In your beauty, how to make poems.
You dance inside my chest, where no one sees you,
but sometimes I do, and that sight becomes this art.

Imagine a boy who has a magical white horse as his best friend. The horse glows with a gentle light, and when the boy is with it, he feels a warm, happy feeling inside his heart. This feeling teaches the boy how to love everything around him—the trees, the stars, even the wind. The horse is so beautiful that it inspires the boy to create poems, as if words just start dancing in his mind. Although no one else can see this magic dance, his poetry demonstrates how love can turn into something beautiful that we can also spread and share with others.

- The poem talks about a white horse whose light teaches a boy how to love. Can you think of why the horse's light might make the boy feel love? How does something beautiful like the horse's light change the way we feel inside?
- In the poem, the boy learns to make poems because of the white horse's beauty. Why do you think seeing something really beautiful, like the horse, can help someone create poems or stories? How does beauty inspire us to make art?
- The poem describes how the white horse dances inside the boy's chest, and only he can see it sometimes. How do you think seeing this invisible dance helps the boy create art? What might it feel like to have something so special inside you that it turns into art when you see it?

Give up to grace.
The ocean takes care
of each wave
till it gets to shore.

This poem is like a gentle reminder that sometimes, we need to let go and trust that things will be okay, just like the ocean takes care of its waves. Imagine you're a wave in the ocean; you don't have to worry about how to get to the shore because the ocean is always there to guide you and make sure you arrive safely. "Give up to grace" means that we should trust in the kindness and support around us, knowing we're being looked after just like the waves. It tells us that it's okay to not have control over everything and to believe that we will be taken care of on our journey, wherever it may lead us.

- The poem talks about the ocean looking after each wave until it reaches the shore. What are some ways you think the ocean helps its waves on their journey to the land? Can you imagine how the wave feels being gently carried by the ocean?
- When the poem says "Give up to grace," it's like saying we should let go and trust that things will be okay. What do you think "grace" might mean in this case? How can we let go and trust more in our lives, like the waves trust the ocean?
- Can you remember a moment when you had to rely on someone else's help or guidance, similar to how the waves depend on the ocean to reach the shore? How did it feel to trust that person or situation, and what happened in the end?

I am so small I can barely be seen.
How can this great love be inside me?
Look at your eyes. They are small,
But they see enormous things.

This poem is like a little puzzle about feeling small but having big feelings or thoughts inside. It's saying, even if someone is small, like a little kid, they can still feel really big love or have big ideas, just like how our tiny eyes can see huge mountains, vast oceans, or the endless sky. The poem makes us wonder how something so big and wonderful can fit inside us when we look so small on the outside. It's kind of like saying that what we are on the inside—our feelings, our dreams, and our love—is much bigger than how we might look on the outside. So, even if you feel small or think you're just a kid, inside you is a huge, amazing world of thoughts and feelings, just waiting to be discovered.

❃ The poem mentions being small but having great love inside. How do you think it's possible for someone who might look small on the outside to hold such big feelings or thoughts inside?

❃ In talking about eyes being small yet seeing enormous things, the poem makes us curious about how we observe the world around us. Why do you think our small eyes can see such vast things, like stars in the sky or wide oceans? What's the most amazing thing you've ever seen, and how did it make you feel?

❃ The poem says that no matter our size, we can experience and understand great things. What are some of the 'enormous things' you believe or dream about, even though you might feel small compared to the whole world? How do these big dreams or feelings fit inside you?

The breeze at dawn has secrets to tell you. Don't go back to sleep.
You must ask for what you really want. Don't go back to sleep
People are going back and forth across the doorsill
where the two worlds touch.
The door is round and open. Don't go back to sleep.

Imagine waking up early when the sun is just starting to peek over the mountains. The first breath of air you take feels different like it's whispering special things just for you. It's like the air has secrets it wants to share, but only if you stay awake and listen closely. In this awake state, the poem encourages us to be brave and ask for the things we truly want in life, just like how you might ask for a special gift for your birthday. But these special things might be even bigger and more surprising than you can imagine, so stay awake and focused. And, It talks about a special doorway where two worlds meet - the world we live in and a magical world all around us you may not know is even there. It's saying, "Stay curious and keep exploring because life has so many wonderful things to show you if you're awake to see them."

❃ Imagine you wake up before anyone else, and the first breath of air feels like it's whispering something special just to you. What kind of secrets do you think the wind might be telling? What would you have to do to hear them clearly?

❃ The poem says not to go back to sleep, even though you might want to. Do you think it means just staying awake in bed, or something else? What are some things you could do besides sleeping that would help you find "what you really want"?

❃ The poem talks about a special doorway where two worlds meet. One world is the one we know, but the other one is maybe magical or full of surprises. Have you ever imagined a secret door like that? Where do you think it might lead, and what kind of adventure awaits on the other side?

When you do things from your soul,
the river itself moves through you.
Freshness and a deep joy are signs of the current.

Imagine you have a magical stream flowing through your heart, just like a tiny river. This poem says that whenever you do something kind or something you really love, like helping a friend or drawing a cool picture, it's like the river is rushing happily inside you. You might feel a tingling feeling throughout your body, or a big smile on your face – those are signs that the happy river is flowing strong! Remember, whenever you do something kind or creative, it's like making the magical river inside you sparkle and shine, bringing joy to you and everyone around you!

✺ When the poem talks about doing things from your soul, it means doing activities that you really, really love, How can you tell when you're doing something from your soul, and what feelings do you notice inside you then?

✺ Think about a moment when you were doing something and you felt great joy. It could be playing, creating something, or helping someone. What were you doing, and why do you think that activity made you feel so good and fresh?

✺ The poem compares the joy you feel when you do things from your heart to a river moving through you. How does imagining a river flowing through you help you understand how special it is to do things you love?

Out beyond ideas of wrongdoing and rightdoing
there is a field. I'll meet you there.
When the soul lies down in that grass
the world is too full to talk about.

Imagine two friends who are arguing and can't agree on something, like what game to play. The poem is like a whisper, telling them that there's a special place far away from their argument, a peaceful field where none of that arguing matters. It's saying, "Let's forget about who's right or wrong and meet in that field." Once they're there, flying a kite together in the beautiful, wide-open space, all their disagreements seem really small and unimportant. Watching their kite dance in the sky, they feel so happy and calm that they don't even want to talk about their fight anymore. The poem is about finding a place of peace and happiness where we can let go of our arguments and just enjoy being together, feeling close and connected without any words.

✺ The poem talks about birds acting in ways that seem like they're searching for us. Why do you think these birds might be trying to send us a message? How can we "hear" what they're saying without understanding bird sounds?

✺ Have you ever seen fish jumping or swimming in a special way? Do you think they might be trying to show us something or answer our questions, even if we don't know what they mean?

✺ The poem says the soul has its own ears to hear things the mind can't understand. Imagine you have a secret sense, like a superpower, that helps you feel happy or excited, even if you don't know why. Do you think you have this special sense, and how can you use it to listen to the world around you in new ways?

What was said to the rose
that made it open
was said to me here
in my chest.

Imagine you have a tiny garden inside your heart, where beautiful flowers of all kinds grow. This poem says that every flower has a special secret whispered to it, making it bloom and be its unique self. It says the same secrets that make the flowers grow are also whispered to you, deep inside your heart. Even though you can't hear them with your ears, you can feel them in your happy thoughts and kind feelings. So, just like the flowers open up to the sunshine, remember to open your heart to all the good things inside you, and let them blossom into something beautiful and special.

❁ What kind of special words or feelings do you think could make a rose bloom, and have you ever heard something similar that made you feel really good and open inside? What words make you feel that way?

❁ Can you remember a time when someone's nice words made you feel a warm, happy glow in your heart, just like the poem describes? How did those words make you feel special or loved?

❁ Why do you think kind and loving words have the power to make us feel bright and open, like a flower showing its petals? How do nice words change the way we see ourselves and others?

Doves when they call coo, are looking for us. Nightingales and parrots
change their perches hoping to be nearer to us.
Word of us reached the fish. They swerved and leapt.
Waves from that stirring keep coming in. The soul has been given
its own ears to hear things that the mind does not understand.

This poem tells a magical story about how animals and fish feel connected to us. When doves coo, they're actually calling out to us, and birds like nightingales and parrots move closer, hoping to be near us. Even fish hear about us and jump with joy, creating waves. The poem says we have a special part inside, called the soul, that can understand these wonderful connections with nature, even if our minds can't always make sense of it. It's like having a magical sense that shows us how everything in nature is connected to us in a beautiful, mysterious way that we feel deep inside, beyond words.

❊ The poem talks about birds acting in ways that seem like they're searching for us. Why do you think these birds might be trying to send us a message? How can we "hear" what they're saying without understanding bird sounds?

❊ Have you ever seen fish jumping or swimming in a special way? Do you think they might be trying to show us something or answer our questions, even if we don't know what they mean?

❊ The poem says the soul has its own ears to hear things the mind can't understand. Imagine you have a secret sense, like a superpower, that helps you feel happy or excited, even if you don't know why. Do you think you have this special sense, and how can you use it to listen to the world around you in new ways?

A mountain keeps an echo
deep inside itself.
That's how I hold your voice.

This poem is like a story about remembering and keeping something very special close to your heart. Imagine an American Indian girl from long ago, who listens to the echoes in the mountains. For her, these echoes feel like the voice of the past, connecting her to her history and ancestors. And just like the mountain holds onto the echo, she keeps their stories deep inside her heart. The poem reminds us that we too can keep the voices and memories of people we care about deep in our hearts, always remembering them and feeling connected, no matter if we are in the past or present.

✂ The poem can remind us of how American Indians might feel connected to their ancestors through voices and echoes in nature. How do you think listening to stories from the past helps us feel connected to our history and ancestors? Why is it important to remember and keep these voices alive in our hearts?

✂ Mountains stand tall for ages, the poem says. Can happy memories stay with you even when they're over? How can you keep these echoes safe inside your heart?

✂ Just like the mountain holds an echo, is there a voice or sound that is very special to you, that you would like to keep close to your heart forever? What makes that voice or sound so important to you?

Let the beauty we love
be what we do.
There are hundreds of ways
to kneel and kiss the ground.

This poem is like a secret code about kindness! It says that the best way to show you love something amazing, like the beauty of the world, isn't just looking at it. It's about taking action and doing things that show that love. Imagine you're at a soup kitchen, where you help by giving food to people who don't have enough to eat. This kind action is a way of showing love and making the world a better place. The poem says there are "hundreds of ways to kneel and kiss the ground," which means there are many different ways to show kindness, just like helping at the soup kitchen. It's like saying every time we help someone, it's a way of thanking the world and making it more beautiful.

✂ How does giving food to people who are hungry at a soup kitchen help show our love for the world and make it a happier place?

✂ If you did something for someone else who really needed help, how do you think it would make them feel?

✂ Besides helping at a soup kitchen, can you imagine another simple act of kindness that could help brighten someone's day and make our world a little bit more beautiful?

Maybe in your loud confusion
the world will disappear and the curtain will lift.
I tell everything, but I do not say it, because, my friend,
it is better that your secret be spoken by you.

This poem is explaining how we get so caught up in noisy and distracting things, like playing on our cell phones, that we might not see the world around us clearly—it's as if everything else just vanishes. But then, it hints that if we stop and listen, we might see things more clearly, like a curtain going up on a stage, showing us what's really important. The poem is also saying, as if a wise friend who knows all about you, that just telling you what you will see isn't as powerful as discovering your own secrets and stories. That makes them even more special. Your wise friend wants you to have the joy of experiencing the world in your own unique way. Your stories and feelings are important, and sharing them with your own voice makes them truly shine!

✳ When we spend a lot of time playing on our cell phones or with other distractions, the poem suggests we might not notice the beautiful and important things happening around us. Why do you think focusing too much on screens can make us miss out on seeing the world and its wonders?

✳ The poem says stopping and listening is like a curtain going up on a stage. Can you think of a movie or show where something amazing happens when a curtain opens? How do you think this relates to paying attention to the world around you?

✳ The poem mentions your wise friend knows all about you, but wants you to discover your own secrets. If you had a magic box full of amazing adventures, would you rather your friend tell you about them or go on them yourself? Why?

The sun's light looks a little different
on this wall than it does on that wall.
And a lot different on this other one,
but it's still one light.

Imagine the sun shining through a stained glass window. Even though it's the same sunlight coming through, each piece of colored glass makes the light look a little different. This poem is saying everyone sees the world around them in their own special way, just like the different colors of light. Just like the sun shines on different walls and makes them look unique, your experiences and perspective make you see things differently from your friends. That's okay. It's a way of showing us that even if we see things differently from others, we're all looking at the same big, important thing, just like we're all under the same sun.

✳ The poem says it's still one light, even though it looks different on each wall. Do you think that means even though we might see things a little differently sometimes, just like the walls, there's still something important that connects us all? What do you think that might be?

✳ Can you remember a time when you saw the same thing differently from someone else? How do you think that can happen? Is it okay if we see the same thing differently?

✳ What does the poem teach us about how our own experiences shape the way we see the world around us?

The moon has opened its face
and its wings made of light.
Borrow eyes to see this,
if yours cannot.

This poem talks about the moon, which sometimes seems like a big, round face in the sky, opening up and spreading its light like beautiful wings. It's saying that if you can't see this magical sight with your own eyes, you might need to borrow someone else's eyes or imagine seeing it in a different way. The poem wants us to open our minds and use our imagination to see the beauty in the world around us, even if we need a little help to do it sometimes. Don't be afraid to ask.

- Sometimes we might need a little help to imagine things, like how the moon turns into a smiling friend with wings. Do you think it's important to keep our imaginations open, even if things seem ordinary at first?
- Can you think of anything else around you that might seem normal but could have a hidden magical side if you looked closer?
- The poem encourages us not to be afraid to ask for help in seeing the beauty around us. Why do you think it's important to sometimes get help from others to see things in a new, magical way? How can sharing what they see help us appreciate the world's beauty more?

Listen to presences inside poems,
Let them take you where they will.
Follow those private hints,

Imagine you're on a treasure hunt! This poem says poems are like secret maps with hidden clues, whispering exciting adventures just waiting to be discovered. It tells you to listen closely to the words and feelings inside the poem, like following the map's arrows. Don't worry if you don't understand everything at first, just keep exploring and see where the poem takes you. It might be on a rocket flying through space or walking through a magical kingdom – the possibilities are endless! It's a way of saying that the adventure and discovery in poems never really end, and we should always be ready to see where they'll take us next. So next time you read a poem, remember, it's an invitation to an amazing adventure. Just listen carefully, follow the clues, and let your imagination take the lead!

- Poems can be like secret maps with clues. How can paying close attention to the words, the pictures they create in your mind, and the feelings they stir up help you solve the poem's mystery and uncover the treasures waiting inside?
- What's one magical adventure or place you'd love to discover through a poem? What clues would you look for inside the poem to guide you there?
- The poem says not to worry if you don't understand everything at first, just keep exploring. Sometimes treasure hunts have tricky riddles or puzzles. If you find a part of the poem that's confusing, what could you do to try and understand it better? Could you ask a grown-up, read it out loud, or maybe even draw a picture based on the words?

As we turn the final page in our journey together, we hope you've found joy, wisdom, and perhaps a new perspective nestled within these pages. If this book has touched your heart, sparked your imagination, and most importantly, inspired conversations with your little ones, we invite you to share your experience. By leaving a review, you can help others discover the magic of poetry, guiding them to works that can enrich the lives of children. Your thoughts and reflections can light the way for others on their quest for meaningful content, just as these poems have illuminated our shared path. Let's create a community of readers dedicated to uncovering the treasures that await in poetry for children, one review at a time!

Please leave a review by visiting our review page with the QR code below, or the review page of the retailer you purchased the book from.
Thanks! DJ

DJ Kadagian brings a unique blend of creativity and insight to his work as a documentary filmmaker, author, and quantum economist. His films, which have been showcased on networks such as PBS, Gaia TV, Discovery Channel, and Hallmark, as well as in over 120 film festivals worldwide, explore a wide range of topics—from socioeconomic issues and race relations to religion, spirituality, alternative healing, and poetry. Kadagian's approach is deeply collaborative, working alongside esteemed philosophers, academics, activists, poets, researchers, and theologians to delve into some of society's most pressing questions.

He is the creator of the film series "Poetry in Motion," an innovative collection of 21 short films. Each film artfully combines a powerful poem with music and imagery, creating a captivating experience. Among his collaborators on this project are Coleman Barks and Robert Bly, and many of the films feature the profound poetry of Rumi. This collection, along with other works, is available for viewing on his website at www.Project-Shift.com, inviting audiences to immerse themselves in a world where poetry comes alive through sound and sight.

CHECK OUT SOME OF DJ'S OTHER WORKS!

What if the existence of life after death could now be answered with certainty? Join us in Crossover Experience as we take you on a journey through 100 of the most exceptional Near-Death Experiences on record and decide for yourself. Death is not an end to our being. It is merely a transition into a different, more expansive existence.

"Portrait of a Radical" explores the revolutionary Jesus Movement, which challenged the power structures of its time. This film uncovers the radical nature of Jesus' mission, revealing a transformative figure whose message remains a beacon of hope for many and a challenge to today's authorities. NEW RELEASE 2024!

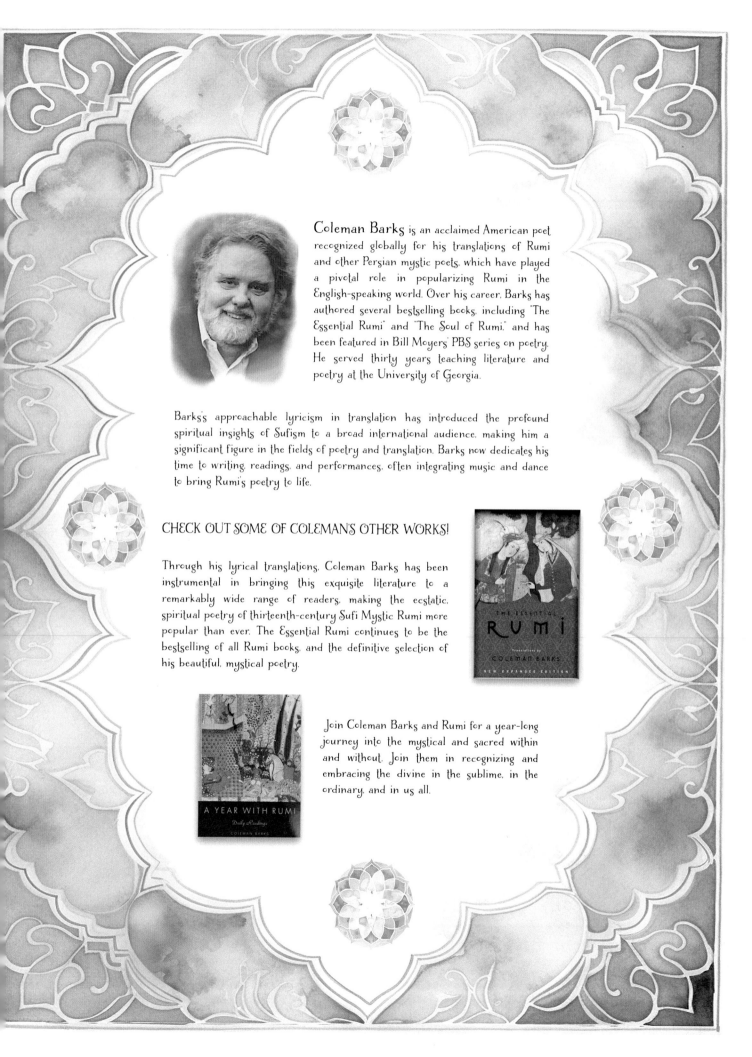

Coleman Barks is an acclaimed American poet recognized globally for his translations of Rumi and other Persian mystic poets, which have played a pivotal role in popularizing Rumi in the English-speaking world. Over his career, Barks has authored several bestselling books, including "The Essential Rumi" and "The Soul of Rumi," and has been featured in Bill Moyers' PBS series on poetry. He served thirty years teaching literature and poetry at the University of Georgia.

Barks's approachable lyricism in translation has introduced the profound spiritual insights of Sufism to a broad international audience, making him a significant figure in the fields of poetry and translation. Barks now dedicates his time to writing, readings, and performances, often integrating music and dance to bring Rumi's poetry to life.

CHECK OUT SOME OF COLEMAN'S OTHER WORKS!

Through his lyrical translations, Coleman Barks has been instrumental in bringing this exquisite literature to a remarkably wide range of readers, making the ecstatic, spiritual poetry of thirteenth-century Sufi Mystic Rumi more popular than ever. The Essential Rumi continues to be the bestselling of all Rumi books, and the definitive selection of his beautiful, mystical poetry.

Join Coleman Barks and Rumi for a year-long journey into the mystical and sacred within and without. Join them in recognizing and embracing the divine in the sublime, in the ordinary, and in us all.

Made in the USA
Las Vegas, NV
08 October 2024